I Love the Holy Land

I Love Jesus

Written by Daniel Cohen & Hanna Nesher
Illustrated by Igor Kovyar
Created & edited by Reuven Dorot
Graphic design by Eti Kalderon
Photography by Reuven Dorot
Cover photograph by Duby Tal - Albatross

© DOKO MEDIA Ltd
ISBN 978-965-478-086-5

Doko is Israel's leading production & distribution company for biblical and historic media products, Doko publish movies, books, music & software.

Published by:
DOKO MEDIA Ltd
10 Moshe Aviv Street, P.O.BOX 611, Or-Yehuda 60371, Israel
Tel: +972 3 6344776 Fax: +972 3 6344690
info@dokomedia.com   Ilovetheholyland@biblelandshop.net

www.biblelandshop.net

One day, a little boy and girl sat together reading a picture book about the Holy Land. They both thought how cool it would be if they could visit the places where the story of Jesus actually happened. Whoosh! Suddenly, the children found themselves right there in the Holy Land...

Mary in Nazareth

It was a quiet morning in the little village of Nazareth. Just like any other day, only something wonderful was about to happen. Suddenly, an angel appeared to a young woman, saying, 'Don't be afraid, Mary, God has chosen you to be the mother of a very special baby boy. He will be the Savior of the world, and you will call him Jesus'.

Jesus' Birth in Bethlehem

The angel's amazing words soon came true! While Mary and Joseph were visiting the town of Bethlehem, the time came for the baby to be born. Because there was nowhere else to stay, Jesus was born in a manger. Wrapped snuggly in soft blankets, Jesus was kept warm by his mother and the animals.

The Three Wise Men

A bright star guided Wise Men from the East to Jesus in the manger. When they saw the baby, they bowed down and worshipped the newborn King, giving him precious gifts of gold, frankincense, and myrrh. Then Mary and Joseph got ready to take Jesus up to Jerusalem.

Jesus' Dedication at the Temple

When Jesus was just a few weeks old, Mary and Joseph brought him up to the Temple in Jerusalem. On their way in, a man named Simeon and a woman named Anna stopped them. The two of them were so happy, because even though Jesus was still just a tiny baby they both recognized him as the promised Savior.

King Herod in Caesarea

Back in Jesus' days, a wicked king named Herod ruled the country of Judea. Herod built the great city of Caesarea on the Mediterranean Sea. But Herod was jealous because the people loved Jesus more than him - so he tried to have Jesus killed.

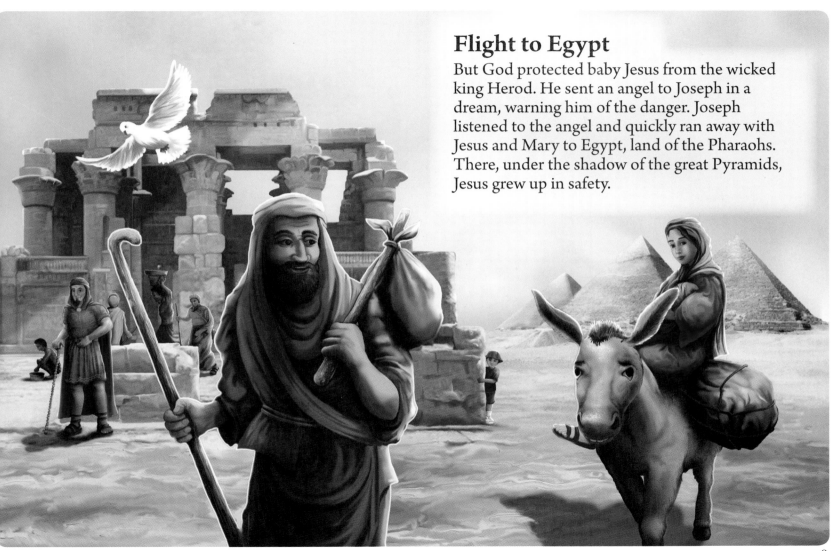

Flight to Egypt

But God protected baby Jesus from the wicked king Herod. He sent an angel to Joseph in a dream, warning him of the danger. Joseph listened to the angel and quickly ran away with Jesus and Mary to Egypt, land of the Pharaohs. There, under the shadow of the great Pyramids, Jesus grew up in safety.

Fields of Nazareth

When Joseph and Mary heard that wicked King Herod was dead, they knew that it was safe to leave Egypt and go back home to Galilee. Here, in the fields of Nazareth, young Jesus grew strong and wise. He probably joined the other children helping in the season of the wheat harvest.

Jerusalem's Holy Temple

Each year, Jesus and his family visited the Holy Temple in Jerusalem to celebrate the festivals. One time, when Joseph and Mary headed home, they noticed that Jesus had disappeared! They were sick with worry. They looked for him everywhere and finally found him back at the Temple, talking with the teachers. They were all amazed at the wisdom of this young boy.

Baptism at the Jordan River

Jesus knew he had special work to do for God. When Jesus was grown, he went to John who was baptizing people in the Jordan River. When Jesus came up from the water, they all saw God's Spirit like a dove and heard a voice saying: 'You are My beloved son and I am very happy with you'.

Mount of Temptation - Jericho

The Holy Spirit led Jesus out into the desert. All alone for forty days and forty nights, he was tested by the devil. Three times Satan tried to tempt Jesus away from the true path of God and three times Jesus resisted the devil's temptations, until Satan finally left. Then angels came to strengthen Jesus.

Wedding at Cana

At a wedding feast in the village of Cana, Jesus performed his first miracle! When the wine ran out, Jesus' mother asked him to do something about it. Jesus asked the servants to fill six stone jars with water and give it to the guests. When they drank it, they all agreed that it was the best wine they had ever tasted!

Sea of Galilee

By the shores of the Sea of Galilee, Jesus began teaching people about the Kingdom of God. Some of the fishermen decided to join Jesus and become his special followers called disciples. Jesus promised to teach them how to 'catch' people for God, instead of catching fish for money.

Capernaum

Jesus soon became known far and wide as a great healer. So many sick people came to him that they couldn't all fit inside the house where he stayed. Some men even climbed onto the roof and lowered their sick friend down into the house. Jesus healed the man and when the crowd saw him walking they were amazed!

Walking on the Water

One day Jesus wanted to pray alone so he sent his disciples off across the Sea of Galilee in a boat, but they got caught in a storm and couldn't move against the wind. Jesus came to help them – walking right on top of the water! The disciples thought it must be a ghost and were afraid but Jesus said, "Don't be scared. It's me, Jesus." Then Jesus told the storm to stop and brought them all safely to shore.

Feeding the Multitudes

Word spread quickly about the wonderful things Jesus was doing. Huge crowds gathered to see him. Once, when the people were hungry, the disciples wanted to send them away to find food but Jesus performed a great miracle: feeding thousands with just a few loaves of bread and a couple of fishes! There was enough food for everyone – and there was even some leftover!

Mt. of Beatitudes

On the Mount of Beatitudes, a hill above the Sea of Galilee, Jesus taught the people many wonderful things about the Kingdom of Heaven. He told the people to love and forgive each other, even their enemies. He also taught them a prayer that we still say today called the Lord's Prayer - Our Father in Heaven, holy is Your name…

Banyas Waterfalls

Jesus went to a beautiful place by the Banyas waterfalls. There, he asked, "Who do people say I am?" The disciples answered him, "Some say you are a great teacher; others say you one of the prophets". But Peter said, "You are the Messiah, the Son of the living God". And Jesus said, "You are right!"

Jesus Loves Little Children

Many people brought their children to be blessed by Jesus. Some of the disciples tried to send them away. They thought that Jesus was too busy to be disturbed by little children. But Jesus loves children, and said that whoever wants to enter the Kingdom of Heaven needs to be just like a little child.

The Good Samaritan

Jesus told a story about a man who was robbed and left on the side of the road to Jerusalem. Some people saw him but simply passed him by. One was too scared. Another was in too much of a hurry. Finally, one man stopped, took the injured man to an inn and even paid for him to be taken care of. Jesus told us that this man, a Samaritan, showed us what it means to be a good neighbor - to love and care for one another.

Gates of Jerusalem

Jesus entered Jerusalem sitting on a young donkey. The crowds welcomed Jesus like a king, spreading their clothes and leafy branches on the road before him. They shouted loudly 'Blessed is he who comes in the name of the Lord!'

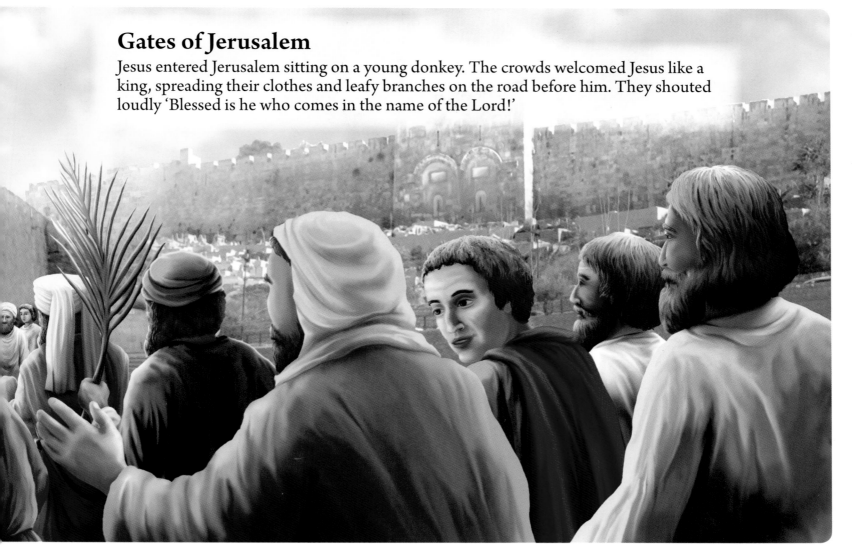

Last Supper Room on Mt. Zion

Jesus and his disciples sat together to celebrate the feast of Passover. Jesus drank a cup of wine and broke the unleavened bread. He knew it would be the last time they would be together, so he said to them, "Whenever you drink wine and eat bread like this from now on, remember me."

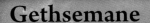

Gethsemane

After their last meal together, Jesus and his disciples went to the Garden of Gethsemane to pray. Jesus didn't want to suffer, but more than this he wanted to do God's will. Soon, Judas came and kissed Jesus, pretending to be his friend. But it was a sign for the soldiers to know who to arrest. One disciple tried to stop the soldiers, but Jesus said, "No, let them take me."

Crucifixion

The soldiers laughed at Jesus and beat him. Then they nailed him to a cross on a hill outside Jerusalem's city walls. Jesus asked God to forgive all the people, saying that they simply didn't know what they were doing.

Jesus goes up to Heaven

After three days, the disciples discovered that Jesus' tomb was miraculously empty. And then Jesus appeared before them both in Jerusalem and in the Galilee. Finally Jesus rose up into the sky to live beside God. He promised that whoever believes in him will also live forever with God in Heaven.